Known CURES
for alcoholism
& other drug addictions

Dr. Ima Teetotaler

Known CURES for alcoholism
& other drug addictions

Copyright © 2007 by Shelly Marshall
ISBN 978-0-9674915-8-5

Retail	$5.00
5 plus copies 30% discount	$3.50
25 plus copies 40% discount	$3.00

Order from:

Day By Day, Recovery Resources
HC 13 Box 4251
Fairview, UT 84629
888 447 1683

Order online:

Retail at Amazon.com
Discounts from Direct Sales at www.day-by-day.org/cubecart

Or order from your favorite recovery bookstore.

This book is dedicated to those searching for the easier, softer way. Stop searching, start writing. Make this your journal of recovery.